ERSEL • LAUGHLIN

P9-CJX-297

JOURNEY OF FAITH

THE STORY OF
THE ARCHDIOCESE OF SEATTLE

Éditions du Signe

ACKNOWLEDGMENTS

The Most Reverend J. Peter Sartain, Archbishop of Seattle

Mary Cross, Ph.D., Seth Dalby, M.A.S., Anne Frederick, Ed.D., Father James O. Johnson, Editorial Committee

Joseph Tancioco, Penny Howell, Patricia Mulhall, Administrative Support

We are grateful to the many people representing the diverse cultures
and religious communities of the Archdiocese of Seattle
whose invaluable insights helped shape this telling of our story.

Editor:

Éditions du Signe
1, rue Alfred Kastler
BP 10094 Eckbolsheim
67038 Strasbourg Cedex - France
Ph.: +33 (0)3 88 78 91 91 - Fax: +33 (0)3 88 78 91 99
www.editionsdusigne.fr
E-mail: info@editionsdusigne.fr

Text: **Corinna LAUGHLIN and Maria LAUGHLIN**

Drawings: **ERSEL**

Colors: **GOTEM**

© 2013 ÉDITIONS DU SIGNE - 109430
All rights reserved - Unauthorised reproduction prohibited
ISBN: 978-2-7468-2966-4

Printed in China

We are the Catholic Church in Western Washington. We are surrounded by the beauty of God's creation. We come from many places, but we are one in the Body of Christ, a pilgrim people journeying to God's kingdom. This is our story.

It's a story of saints and sinners; of native peoples and newcomers, of missionaries and teachers, working side by side to build the church in Western Washington. It's a story of adventure, invention, and tradition. It's a story of spirit and sacrifice for the glory of God.

Long before the Catholic faith came to this land, native peoples--Nisqually, Makah, Lummi, Puyallup, Muckleshoot, Tlingit, Nez Perce--lived here. They worshipped the great Spirit and called this land sacred ground. Five hundred generations came and went.

Then newcomers came, white Europeans. The native peoples were curious about their ways, and wondered why they had come.

Spanish explorers sailed past what is now Washington State in the ship Santiago*. The first Catholics set foot on these shores and left a cross behind. Captain Vancouver explored Puget Sound.

The whites kept coming. They brought new ideas and new diseases. And they brought a new teaching about God.

Chief Si'ahl (Seattle) was born in 1780 on the Duwamish.

*Santiago=St. James

4

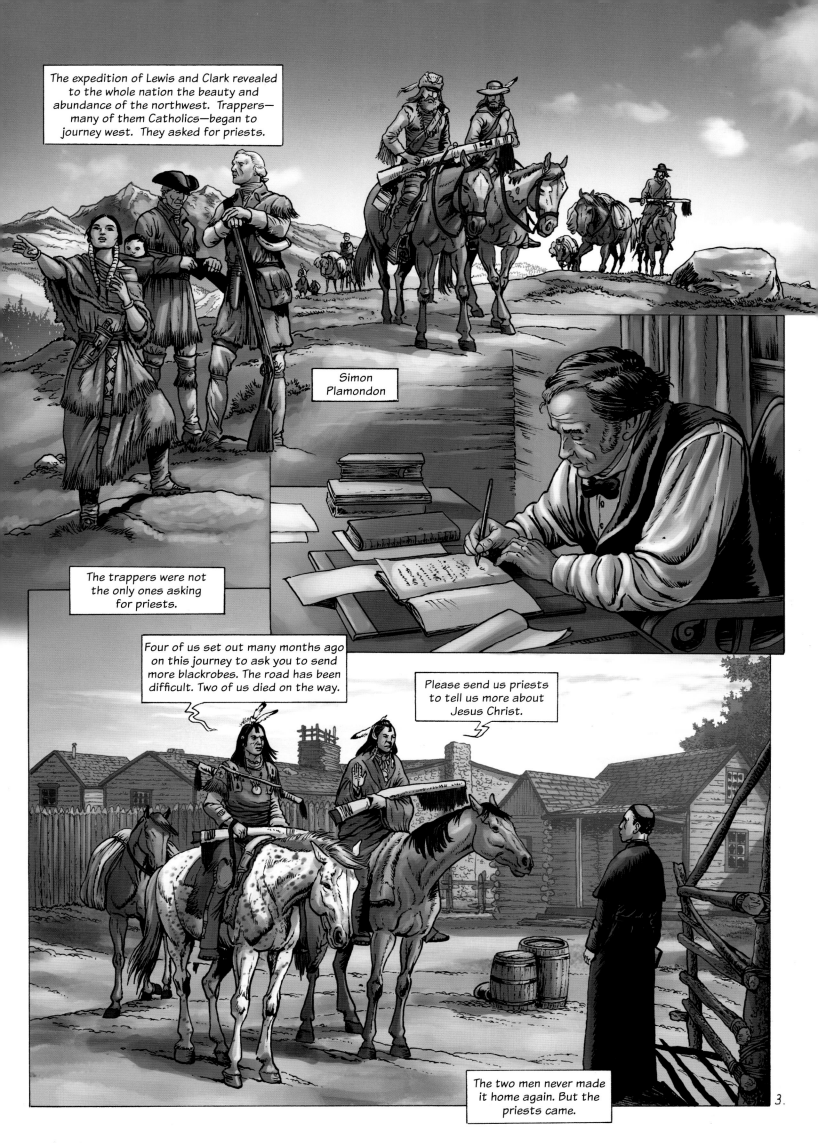

The expedition of Lewis and Clark revealed to the whole nation the beauty and abundance of the northwest. Trappers—many of them Catholics—began to journey west. They asked for priests.

Simon Plamondon

The trappers were not the only ones asking for priests.

Four of us set out many months ago on this journey to ask you to send more blackrobes. The road has been difficult. Two of us died on the way.

Please send us priests to tell us more about Jesus Christ.

The two men never made it home again. But the priests came.

3.

Not only the Catholics, but many others came to listen to the singing and the preaching.

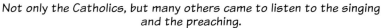

I must learn their language if I am to share the Gospel with them.

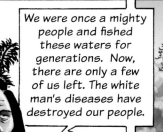

We were once a mighty people and fished these waters for generations. Now, there are only a few of us left. The white man's diseases have destroyed our people.

There are so many languages. How can we preach the Gospel without using words?

The native peoples tell stories using carved wooden poles, with images and symbols. I wonder if we could create a pole to tell the story of salvation.

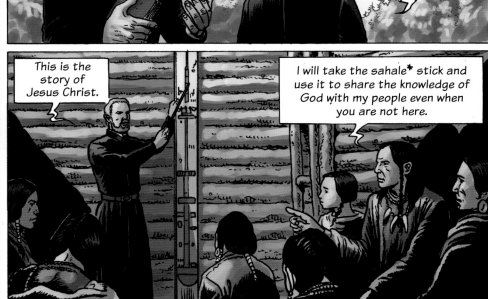

This is the story of Jesus Christ.

I will take the sahale* stick and use it to share the knowledge of God with my people even when you are not here.

stick from heaven

7

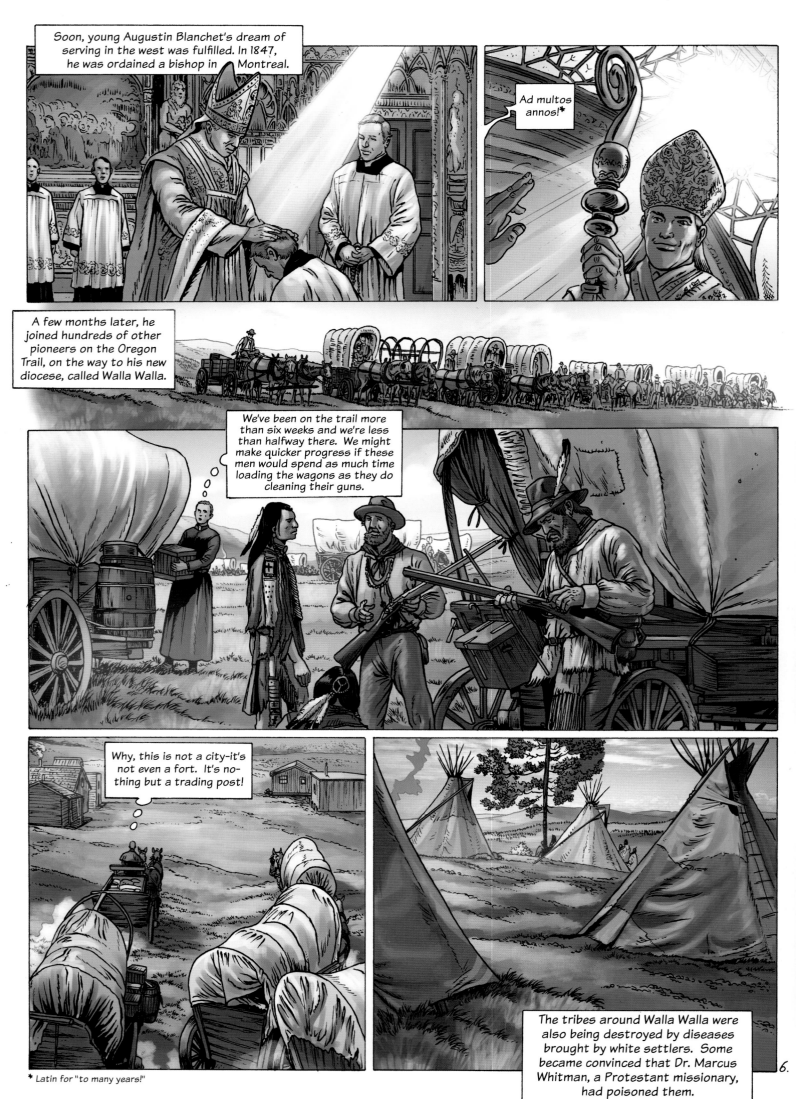

Soon, young Augustin Blanchet's dream of serving in the west was fulfilled. In 1847, he was ordained a bishop in Montreal.

Ad multos annos!*

A few months later, he joined hundreds of other pioneers on the Oregon Trail, on the way to his new diocese, called Walla Walla.

We've been on the trail more than six weeks and we're less than halfway there. We might make quicker progress if these men would spend as much time loading the wagons as they do cleaning their guns.

Why, this is not a city–it's not even a fort. It's nothing but a trading post!

The tribes around Walla Walla were also being destroyed by diseases brought by white settlers. Some became convinced that Dr. Marcus Whitman, a Protestant missionary, had poisoned them.

* Latin for "to many years!"

6.

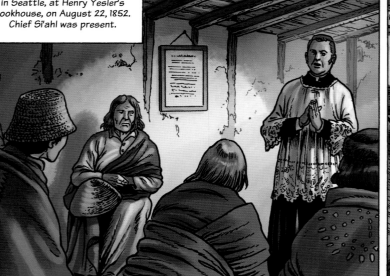

In spite of setbacks, the faith continued to spread. Bishop Demers offered the first Mass in Seattle, at Henry Yesler's cookhouse, on August 22, 1852. Chief Si'ahl was present.

Meanwhile, Father Eugene Chirouse, OMI*, ministered among the native peoples all over Puget Sound. He translated prayers and scriptures into native languages. When the Lummi people were confined to a reservation, he went with them.

We are so poor here that we must be ingenious. My school and chapel are simple huts. My thurible is made of rope and tin! I have my accordion with me and in the evenings, when my work is done, I play a bit to keep my spirits up.

The sense of the Divine Presence is here, no less than in many a dim cathedral far away.

Now our people say, 'that happened before Father Chirouse came, or that happened after Father Chirouse came.' He is the friend of the Lummi people.

8.

* An Oblate priest

Esther's father was right. Esther became Sister Joseph. When Bishop Blanchet came asking for sisters to help him in Vancouver, she volunteered with four other sisters. With Bishop Blanchet and a volunteer priest, Father Luigi Rossi, they traveled a long way—by boat, by train, by boat, and on foot, before they at last reached faraway Vancouver.

Welcome home, Your Excellency. Welcome, Sisters. I will lead you to the cathedral.

How far is it to the cathedral?

About a mile.

What is this shanty?

It is the bishop's palace.

We have our work cut out for us!

Puget Sound is growing quickly. Go north and minister to the Catholics on the Sound.

I would like to go to Seattle--I think it has great promise.

Don't waste your time there, Father Prefontaine. Seattle is a lost cause.

I will go to the capital, in Olympia.

Father Rossi's Church of the Immaculate Conception, Steilacoom.

Father Luigi Rossi arrives in Olympia.

This is the future. There is no limit to how Seattle will grow if we can get people to settle here.

Father Prefontaine's Church of our Lady of Good Help, Seattle.

Princess Angeline, daughter of Chief Seattle, was one of Father Prefontaine's first parishioners.

I am a Catholic, and I have a crucifix and a rosary. This is my friend.

12.

So much has changed since we came here as young men. I am old and weary. It is time for me to step down. I have asked the Holy Father to send Portland a new Archbishop.

After all the years of building, growth, and struggle, I, too, am ready for a rest.

Aegidius Junger succeeded Blanchet as the Bishop of Nesqually.

The new bishop doesn't take as strong a hand as Bishop Blanchet did with the territorial government.

But he is a good, kind man, who cares for the little ones. Already, he is well-loved by the people.

In 1885, Bishop Junger dedicated a new St. James Cathedral in Vancouver.

It is one of the largest and most beautiful churches in the entire Northwest.

Archbishop Gross of Portland preached at the dedication Mass.

Now that's what I call a sermon-- 90 minutes!

13.

Bishop Junger oversaw the building of many churches and schools.

Father Hylebos and old St. Leo's, Tacoma.

Holy Names Academy, Seattle.

Founding of Seattle College, 1891.

St. Martin's College in Lacey opened with just one student, Angus McDonald.

Bishop Junger died at Providence Hospital in Vancouver on December 26, 1896. Mother Joseph was by his side.

14.

Times were changing. Seattle continued to grow. With growth came challenges—especially prejudice. In 1882, the Chinese Exclusion Act became law.

What does it mean?

It means that no more Chinese can come to the United States. They don't want us here.

DECLARATION

On February 7, 1886, an angry mob drove the Chinese of Seattle out of town. The bell of the Catholic Church rang out a warning.

DONG DONG DONG

Princess Angeline died in May, 1896. It was the end of an era.

How Seattle has changed and grown. On these streets where I cleared away the stumps of old forests, a bustling city has arisen. Whoever the new bishop is, I hope he will consider moving here.

15.

The Seattle P-I proclaimed Bishop O'Dea to be "one of the youngest as well as one of the best-looking prelates in the United States"!

Soon after Bishop O'Dea's consecration came big news from the north.

There's gold in Alaska. A boat just docked in Seattle with a ton of gold –

a TON of GOLD!

Soon 100,000 prospectors came through Seattle to try their luck in Alaska. The population of Seattle exploded.

Meanwhile, in Vancouver...

Mother is failing. She is in such pain.

But she still keeps chocolates to give the young ones who come and pray the rosary with her.

Sisters, whatever concerns the poor is always our affair.

What shall I do without her friendship and her wise counsel? May she rest in peace.

Mother Joseph died on January 19, 1902.

17

Plans proceeded rapidly with the design by Heins and LaFarge of New York City. The cornerstone was laid on November 12, 1905.

I feel as if a new life has been born in Seattle on this day of the laying of the cornerstone of the big cathedral.

December 22, 1907. The day of the Cathedral's dedication.

Is it possible to get a seat?

A seat? There's not an inch of room to stand in, let alone sit!

Dr. Franklin Sawyer Palmer, the first organist of St. James Cathedral.

Martina Johnston was the first editor of the Catholic Northwest Progress.

Can you tell me how you feel today, Bishop?

Proud! I might even say, very proud.

19.

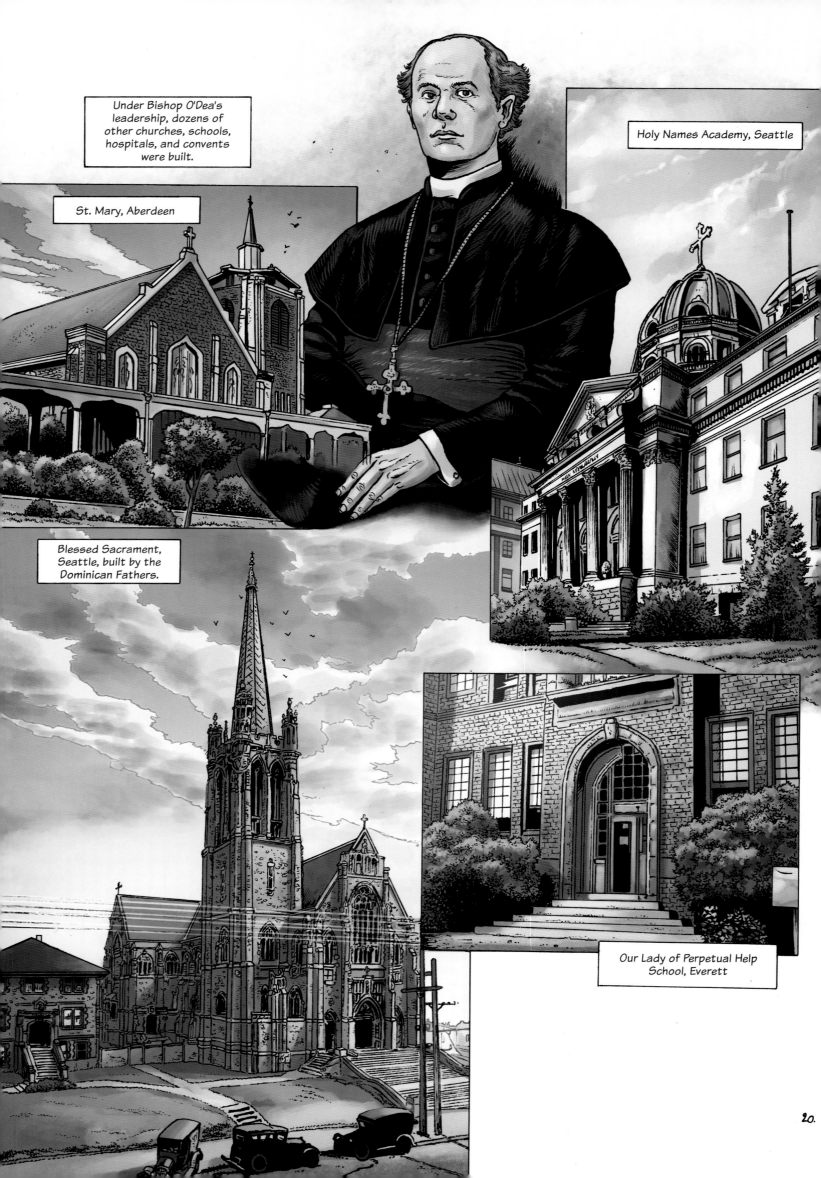

Under Bishop O'Dea's leadership, dozens of other churches, schools, hospitals, and convents were built.

Holy Names Academy, Seattle

St. Mary, Aberdeen

Blessed Sacrament, Seattle, built by the Dominican Fathers.

Our Lady of Perpetual Help School, Everett

20.

Soon, the Church in western Washington had a flourishing Catholic school system.

The school day always began with prayer.

There was the morning offering and the pledge of allegiance.

There was lots of learning—reading, math, science, music, penmanship.

Students memorized everything from the ca-techism to poetry by Long-fellow, Wordsworth, and other favorites.

...We can make our lives sublime, / And, departing, leave behind us / Footprints on the sands of time...

21.

There was time for fun, too.

And there was always more prayer at the end of the day!

24

1903. Mother Frances Xavier Cabrini arrives to minister to Italian immigrants in Seattle.

The Bishop here is very good. His name is O'Dea. He is happy to have us because we bear the name of the Sacred Heart of Jesus.

Excuse me, sir, what is this building?

Why, that's the Perry Hotel, one of the finest hotels in Seattle.

It would make a wonderful hospital. I will talk to the owner.

Soon, the Perry Hotel became the Columbus Hospital. Mother Cabrini's motto was, "I can do all things through Christ who gives me strength" (Philippians 4:1).

Years later, a miraculous healing would take place at Columbus Hospital that that would help make Mother Cabrini a saint.

Mother Cabrini became a U.S. citizen in Seattle.

Mother Cabrini is one of the greatest women of the twentieth century. She will be a saint one day.

23.

There was building, and rebuilding. On February 2, 1916....

BOOM

Thank God, no one was hurt. But please, not a word of this to the press!

Father William Noonan, Cathedral Pastor.

THE POST-INTELLIG...

CATHEDRAL DOME FALLS

CRASHES UNDER SNOW'S WEIGHT

LOSS $75,00...

We must accept it resignedly from the hands of God, who will, in his own good time, convert our sorrow into joy.

I'm not Catholic, but I want to contribute to the repairs of our city's beautiful cathedral.

I think we can say that a more beautiful temple has replaced the old.

24.

Lay people were very involved in their Church. Thousands belonged to groups that met monthly, focused on prayer and holiness of life.

Children of Mary

Catholic Daughters of America

Holy Name Society

Knights of Columbus

There were also groups focused on service of the poor.

In 1918, the Seattle Council of Catholic Women began an outreach to the poor, especially children and families. Their work would eventually become Catholic Community Services, the largest private social service provider in the state.

1920, old St. Benedict's Church, Seattle.

The mission of the Society of St. Vincent de Paul is to help the poor through home visits. It's high time we had some Vincentians in the northwest.

The Diocese of Seattle was becoming home to more and more diverse cultures. Bishop O'Dea invited the Maryknoll Missioners to come and minister to Japanese and Filipino Catholics. The Sisters came first...

...then the priests.

Our Lady Queen of Martyrs Church and School, Seattle

There is great hunger for God among the Asian peoples.

CATHOLIC FILIPINO CLUB

My family's faith has its roots in that time of persecution, hundreds of years ago.

26.

29

The Japanese have bombed Pearl Harbor. This is a day that will live in infamy.

In these momentous hours, let us embrace our fellow American citizens of Japanese extraction in a special bond of charity...*

But other voices prevailed. Executive Order 9066 ordered the internment of all American citizens of Japanese descent. The parish of Our Lady Queen of Martyrs was torn apart as the Japanese Catholics were interned in camps in Washington, Idaho, and California. Father Leo Tibesar, MM, their pastor, went with them.

IS THIS AMERICA?

Dear Bishop, thank you for your support. I am exerting what pressure I can to obtain a modicum of that religious freedom which we have in such quantities to export to all the nations of the earth.

It is so good to have Father Tibesar with us. It is almost like being at home at Queen of Martyrs.

If it were not for him and the sisters, I would feel that everyone back home had forgotten us.

*Bishop Shaughnessy's letter was read from every pulpit in the diocese.

29.

August 6, 1945, St. Edward's Seminary.

The atom bomb has been dropped on Hiroshima...

Dutch, have you heard? It sounds as though the war will be over soon.

I heard it, but I can hardly believe it. How could one bomb kill so many people?

Raymond Hunthausen, future Archbishop of Seattle.

November, 1945. Bishop Shaughnessy suffered a severe stroke on his way home from a meeting of US bishops in Washington, DC. He would never be the same.

1948. Pope Pius XII appointed young Thomas Arthur Connolly, auxiliary of San Francisco as coadjutor bishop.

Bishop Shaughnessy died on Ascension Thursday, May 18, 1950.

30.

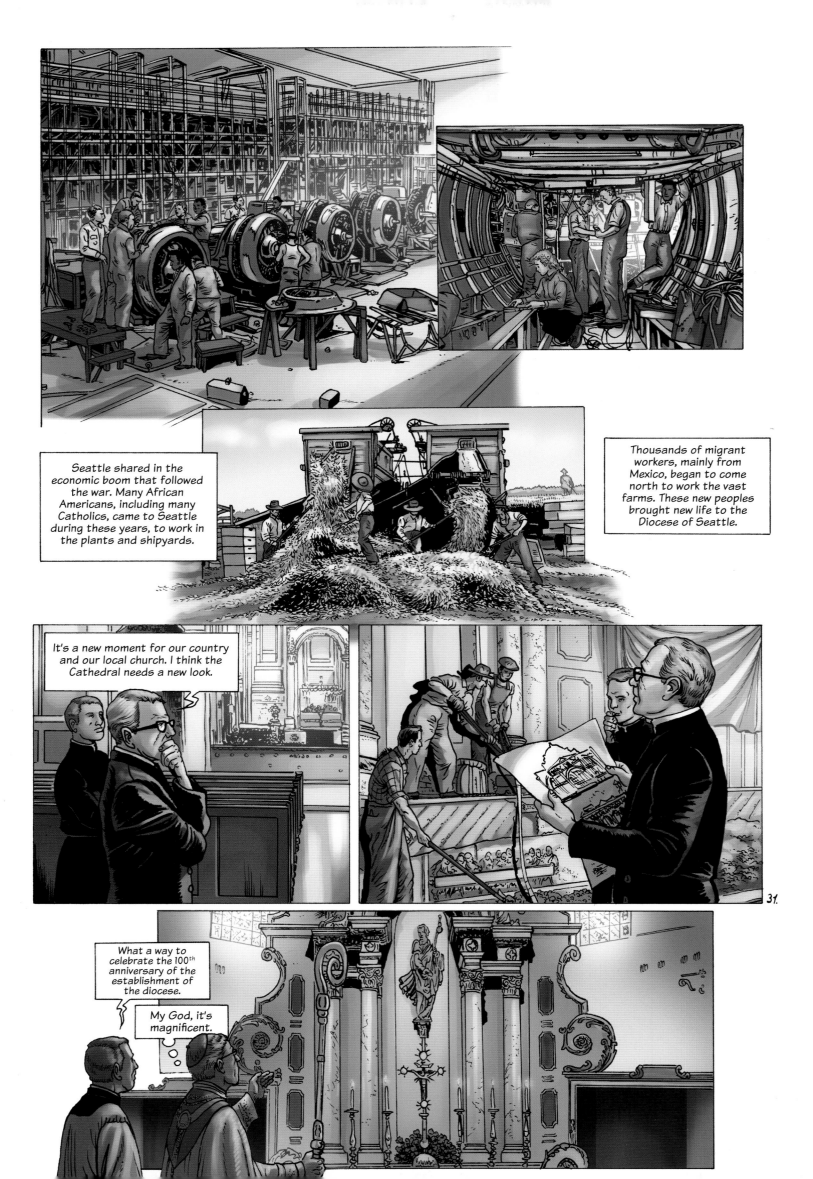

The diocese of Yakima was created in 1951. At the same time, Pope Pius XII elevated Seattle to an Archdiocese. Connolly became the first Archbishop of Seattle.

Archbishop Connolly built and built. Times had changed – and churches started to look different, too.

Our Lady of the Lake, north Seattle

St. Edward, south Seattle

GALLAGHER

St. Thomas Major Seminary, Kenmore

Children and young people deepen faith, community, and respect for God's creation at CYO (Catholic Youth Organization) summer camps

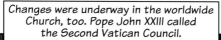

Changes were underway in the worldwide Church, too. Pope John XXIII called the Second Vatican Council.

That I should live to see a day such as this! How good is the good God.

The Council met each fall for four years, and the bishops discussed virtually every aspect of church life and teaching. In October, 1965, Archbishop Connolly addressed the Council.

It was a far cry from the little house in San Francisco where I first saw the light of day 66 years ago, to the Patriarchal Basilica... I shall not soon forget it. However, I was glad when the ordeal was over.

Back in Seattle, the work of implementing the reforms began.

The successful attainment of the council's aims and purposes will depend, to a certain extent, on you, and you, and you—on the manner in which you translate, in your daily lives, the decrees and declarations.

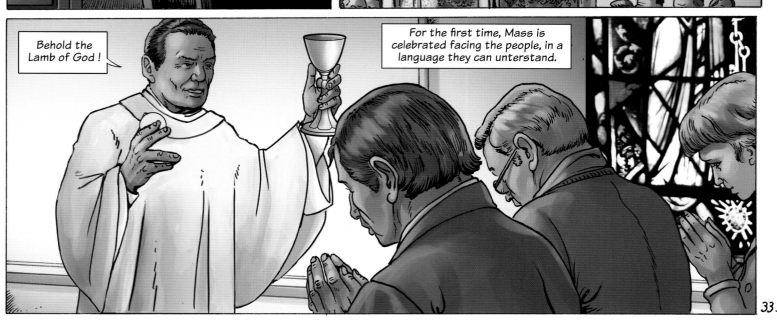

Behold the Lamb of God !

For the first time, Mass is celebrated facing the people, in a language they can unterstand.

33.

In spite of progress, there was still great intolerance. Seattle Rabbi Raphael Levine approached Archbishop Connolly with a bold idea.

I have a dream of a television program where a rabbi, a Catholic priest, and a Protestant minister sit down and talk about the issues of the day without anger or prejudice.

Father William Treacy is the man for the job.

Every Sunday for 14 years, 300,000 people tuned in to listen to their conversations about questions like "Who was responsible for Jesus' death?" and "Celebrating Christmas in public schools."

Father Treacy and Rabbi Levine became lifelong friends. Together they established Camp Brotherhood, dedicated to religious tolerance.

Archbishop Connolly was a vocal advocate for civil rights. In Seattle, blacks and other minorities were only allowed to purchase property in certain parts of the city.

In February, 1968, the Catholics hosted the Interfaith Civil Rights Banquet. Two thousand people came.

We want open housing legislation, with teeth in it!

We've never seen a gathering like this in Seattle!

34.

April 4, 1968. Dr. Martin Luther King, Jr. was assassinated. That Sunday, Archbishop Connolly led a great procession from St. James Cathedral which joined with others from across the city, and gathered at the Seattle Center in remembrance of Dr. King.

Archbishop Connolly advocated for the rights of migrant workers.

I will encourage all Catholics to join me in the boycott of growers who do not respect worker's rights. Farm workers have the lowest annual income of all our nation's working people.

Archbishop Connolly retired in 1975.

He was a bricks and mortar bishop, a real builder.

He certainly was. Since he came to Seattle 27 years ago, Catholics have built 84 churches, 38 schools and more than 200 meeting halls, education centers, convents and rectories, as well as summer camps, seminaries and cemeteries. "Bricks and mortar" is an understatement!

35.

Pope Paul VI appointed Raymond Hunthausen to succeed Archbishop Connolly. He was no stranger to Seattle: a Montana native, he had studied at St. Edward's Seminary. He was filled with the excitement of the Second Vatican Council, and with a great passion for peace. Archbishop Hunthausen spoke out boldly against the escalating arms race. His decision to withhold half of his income tax gained national attention and caused controversy.

In the wake of the Vietnam war, Seattle welcomed an influx of Vietnamese refugees in the 1970s and 1980s.

36.

Archbishop Hunthausen ordained permanent deacons for their ministry of service.

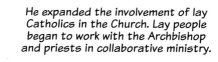

He expanded the involvement of lay Catholics in the Church. Lay people began to work with the Archbishop and priests in collaborative ministry.

Archbishop Hunthausen was the subject of an Apostolic Visitation* for some controversial areas of his ministry. He continued to lead the diocese through painful and divisive times. His simple, humble approach won the love of many.

Nonviolence requires at least as much of our lives as war does.... I am challenged by the nonviolent truth of the cross, by the calling of the God of Love to lose our lives for peace.

*Apostolic visitation=a special investigation by the Vatican.

In 1987, Thomas J. Murphy was appointed coadjutor Archbishop of Seattle.

37.

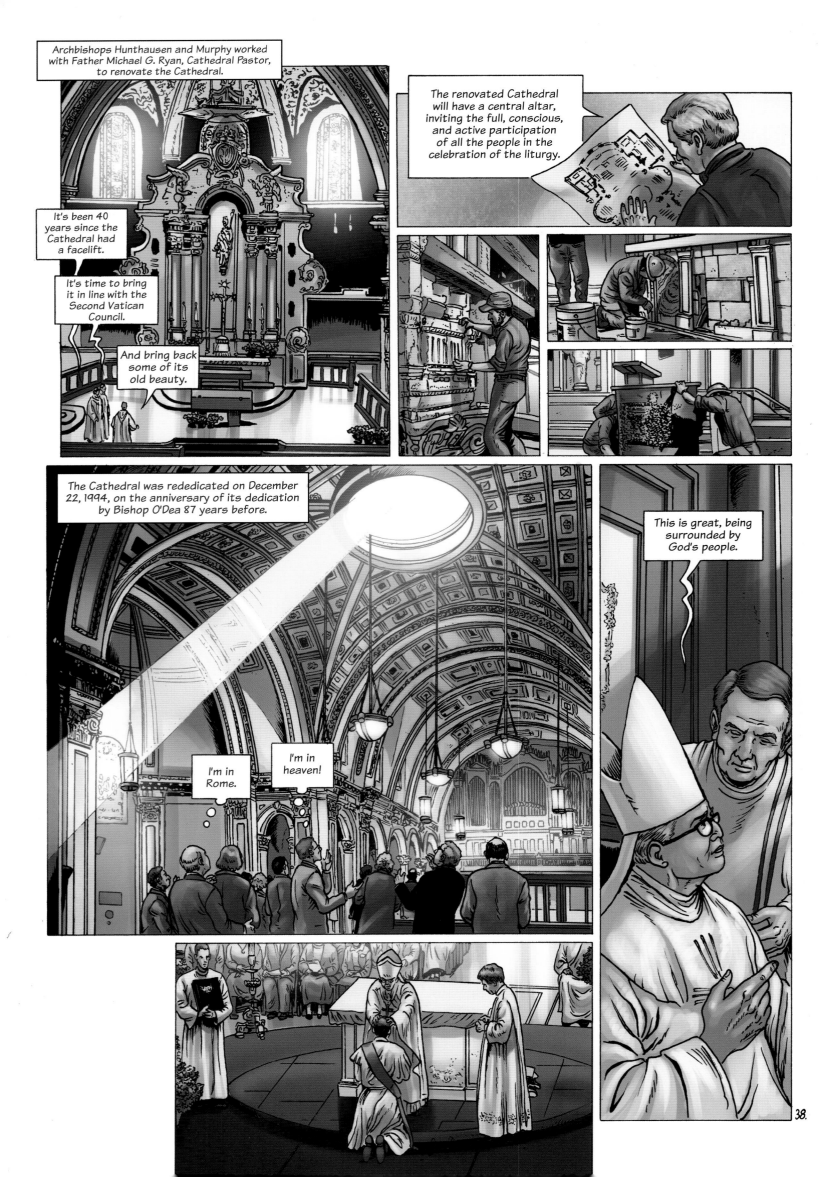

Archbishop Murphy was known for his tireless traveling up and down the Archdiocese. He was diagnosed with leukemia in the fall of 1996.

He was laid to rest in the Cathedral he loved on July 3, 1997.

Facing the reality of death, I know I must be a steward of the gift of life. Gratitude has become a way of life for me. Each morning when I awake, I thank God for this gift I assumed I would always have.

Under his leadership, ministry to the diverse people of Seattle continued to expand. The first Mass he celebrated was Simbang Gabi, the celebration of Advent from the Philippines.

On December 17, 1997, Archbishop Alexander J. Brunett was installed.

He also celebrated the Lunar New Year with the Vietnamese community.... And Madre de las Americas* with Hispanic people from across the Archdiocese.

*Mother of the Americas.

Making the sign "CHRIST"
in American sign language

In 1998, "Open Wide the Doors to Christ"
appeared, including people with disabilities
in the ministries of the Church.

In 2005, two local priests were ordained
auxiliary bishops for the Archdiocese:
Eusebio Elizondo and Joseph Tyson.
They brought years of experience in the
multicultural Church of the Pacific Northwest.

At a time when many dioceses were forced
to close their Catholic schools, two new high
schools were built under Archbishop Brunett's
leadership. The innovative Fulcrum Foundation
was established to ensure that children of the
future would have access to Catholic education.

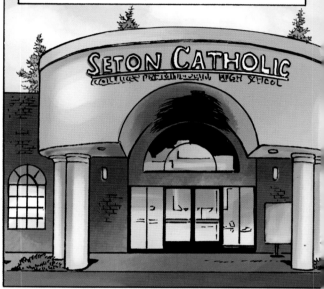

In 2006, Jake Finkbonner, a young
student at Assumption School in
Bellingham, contracted flesh-eating
bacteria. He almost died. His pastor,
Father Tim Sauer, encouraged the family
to pray to Blessed Kateri Tekakwitha since
they were part of the Lummi tribe.

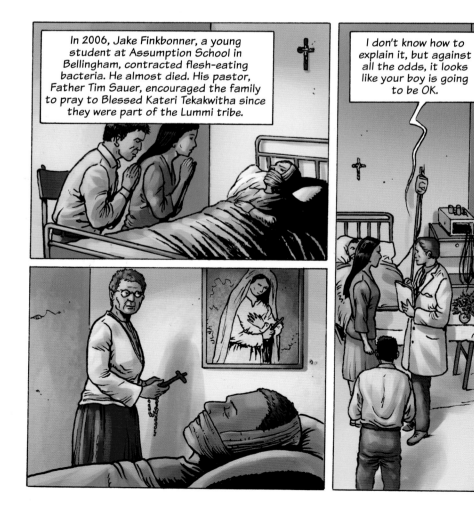

I don't know how to
explain it, but against
all the odds, it looks
like your boy is going
to be OK.

Jake's healing led to Kateri's
canonization.

If it weren't for
her, I wouldn't
be here.

40.

Archbishop Sartain arrived as the ninth bishop, fifth Archbishop of Seattle on December 1, 2010.

Every day in this local Church...

People worship God.

The poor are fed, clothed, and housed.

Children grow in faith in our Catholic schools.

Sacraments are celebrated.

Bishops, priests, deacons, religious, and laypeople all work side by side to proclaim the Gospel of Jesus Christ and build the Kingdom. We are all part of this pilgrimage that began so long ago, and continues today. What is your part in this great story?

[Appendix]

A PLACE FOR MANY PEOPLES

From the very beginning, the Pacific Northwest has been a meeting-place for many different peoples. The Catholic Church has been part of that encounter for more than two centuries. Among the first Europeans to come in contact with the Native Americans of the Pacific Northwest were two Franciscan priests on board the Spanish ship Santiago, which sailed past the Washington coast in July of 1774.

The first interactions were quite friendly. But that was not to be the case for long. As white settlers came in increasing numbers, the Native American peoples were gradually pushed off of their traditional lands. The whites also brought new diseases which were fatal to the native peoples, including smallpox, measles, and tuberculosis. The missionaries who brought the Christian faith — both Catholic and Protestant — were sometimes harsh in the way they suppressed the tribal religious beliefs. In 1856, Isaac Stevens, the governor of Washington Territory, declared a "war of extermination" on the native peoples. That violent conflict dragged on for years in what is called the Puget Sound War.

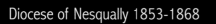

Diocese of Nesqually 1853-1868

Chief Seattle, photographed by E. M. Sammis, 1864.
(Museum of History & Industry, Seattle. All rights reserved)

People of many different races and backgrounds continued to come to the Pacific Northwest in search of a better life. In the early settlements, people of different races often lived and worked peacefully, side by side. But the Northwest also has a long history of racial prejudice, escalating at times to violence. Chinese immigrants, at first welcomed because they provided cheap labor, became targets of bigotry and hate when the economy experienced a downturn in the late 1870s.

In 1886, a Seattle mob rounded up the Chinese and forced them to board a steamer. When the ship was full, two hundred Chinese people were still left on shore, and a riot broke out in which many were injured. Within a few months, there were almost no Chinese left in the Pacific Northwest.

More than fifty years later, in the weeks following the bombing of Pearl Harbor, the Japanese community of the Northwest were ostracized, taken from their homes and sent to internment camps in Idaho and California. Communities and families were shattered.

Empty desks at Seattle's Bailey Gatzert School following the internment of Japanese-Americans in 1942.
(Seattle Post-Intelligencer Collection, Museum of History & Industry, Seattle. All rights reserved)

In both these instances, the Catholic Church was a force for good as the bells of Our Lady of Good Help Church rang a warning for the Chinese people in 1886, and the Maryknoll priests offered support for the Japanese Americans during World War II. Today, the Church continues to speak out on behalf of all who are most vulnerable in our communities, and to advocate for religious freedom.

- How has the Church welcomed people of different races and languages? Have there been times when the Church has not welcomed newcomers?
- As you read about the history of the Japanese internment during World War II, imagine yourself as a young person taken from your home and moved to a faraway camp. How would you feel?
- What needs to change if we are not to repeat the mistakes of the past?

Princess Angeline, daughter of Chief Seattle, ca. 1890. (Museum of History & Industry, Seattle. All rights reserved)

CHANGING BOUNDARIES

Diocese of Seattle 1868-1913

The Catholic Archdiocese of Seattle now serves the western part of Washington State, from the Pacific Ocean on the west to the crest of the Cascade Mountains on the east. Both the size and the name of the diocese have changed several times as the Catholic Church has sought to serve the people of the Pacific Northwest in the most effective and efficient way possible.

In 1843, Pope Gregory XVI named Francis Norbert Blanchet the bishop of an enormous "apostolic vicariate" which included present-day Oregon, Washington, British Columbia, and Alaska, and which extended from the Pacific Ocean clear to the Rocky Mountains. By 1846, this immense territory had been divided into smaller areas—Modest Demers became the first Bishop of Vancouver Island, while F. N. Blanchet's brother, Augustin Magloire Alexandre Blanchet, became the first Bishop of Walla Walla, later Nesqually, later Seattle. So little was known about the region at the time that there was a considerable amount of guesswork involved in the naming of these ecclesiastical territories.

Bishop A. M. A. Blanchet was the first bishop of the diocese of Nesqually, later Seattle. (Courtesy of the Archives of the Catholic Archdiocese of Seattle)

In 1853, the Diocese of Nesqually included all of Washington State, and much of what is now Idaho and Montana. The fastest way to cross this enormous terrain was on horseback, though later on, stagecoaches would make it somewhat easier for the bishop to move around the diocese to meet with priests, dedicate churches and celebrate the sacraments.

In 1868, the diocese was reduced in size to encompass all of Washington Territory. At that time, Washington had a number of thriving cities. When Bishop O'Dea was appointed in 1896, the citizens of Seattle, Tacoma, and Spokane all wrote to him to encourage him to relocate the cathedral to their cities. He decided to build in Seattle, and at the same time St. James Cathedral was built—1907— the name of the diocese was changed from Nesqually to Seattle.

Bishop Edward O'Dea served the diocese more than thirty years - longer than any other bishop to date. (Courtesy of the Archives of the Catholic Archdiocese of Seattle)

In 1913, the diocese of Spokane was created, and finally, in 1951, the diocese of Yakima was carved out, while the Diocese of Seattle was elevated to an Archdiocese. The changing map of the Archdiocese of Seattle reflects the growth of Washington State, and the growth of the faith as well. Today, our diocese is smaller geographically but much larger in its Catholic population: it covers 28,731 square miles and serves more than half a million Catholics.

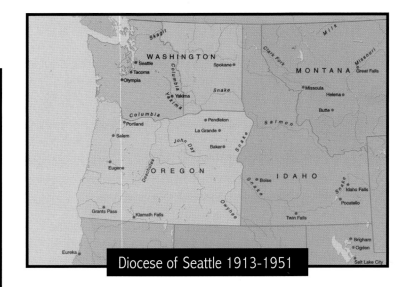

Diocese of Seattle 1913-1951

St. James Cathedral towers over early Seattle in this 1908 photo. (Courtesy of St. James Cathedral)

- **Some of our Catholic churches are built in prominent locations—on hilltops where they are visible from far away. Others are nestled in valleys where they blend in with the beautiful trees and landscape of the Pacific Northwest. Look at your parish church. Where is it located? Why it was built in that particular spot? What part has it played in the life of the local community?**
- **Make a pilgrimage to St. James Cathedral, or to one of the other historic churches around the Archdiocese.**

RELIGIOUS COMMUNITIES

From the time of Bishop Blanchet to the present, the bishops of the Archdiocese of Seattle have invited religious communities to work alongside them. The Society of Jesus (Jesuits) and the Oblates of Mary Immaculate were among the first to arrive. Later came Benedictines, Dominicans, Carmelites, Redemptorists, and Maryknoll priests. More recently, the Archdiocese has welcomed priests from the Society of Christ (Poland), Domus Dei Clerical Society (Vietnam) and the Missionaries of the Holy Spirit (Mexico), among others.

Women religious have played an enormous part in the building up of the Church in the Pacific Northwest. The first to arrive were the Sisters of Providence, led by the indefatigable Mother Joseph. They were followed soon afterwards by the Sisters of the Holy Names of Jesus and Mary. Within a few decades, there were dozens of communities working in the Pacific Northwest, in schools, hospitals, orphanages, and many other institutions. Today, women religious representing twenty-eight different communities serve in the Archdiocese of Seattle.

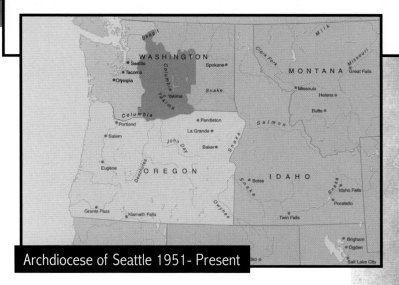

Archdiocese of Seattle 1951- Present

Portrait of Mother Joseph from about the time she came from Montreal to Vancouver. (Courtesy of Providence Archives, Seattle, Washington.)

Carpentry tools used by Mother Joseph.
(Courtesy of Providence Archives, Seattle, Washington)

- **What are some of the different ministries carried out by religious communities in the Archdiocese of Seattle?**
- **Why are there so many different religious communities? Interview a religious sister or priest and find out why they joined the community they did.**

LIVING HISTORY

Where do you find the history of the Archdiocese of Seattle? In creating this book, the writers and illustrators drew on many different sources.

Primary Sources. There are many first-hand accounts of different parts of our history. Bishop Blanchet kept a diary (in his native language, French) that tells of his experiences on the Oregon Trail. There are also many official documents—letters and official statements of the bishop— which are kept in the Archives of the Archdiocese of Seattle. Examples of these are Bishop O'Dea's letters about building St. James Cathedral, and Bishop Shaughnessy's statement on the internment of Japanese Americans.

There are other archives, too. One of the largest belongs to the Sisters of Providence, who have hundreds of objects, like Mother Joseph's tabernacle, chronicles written by the Sisters as well as thousands of photos. The Sisters of the Holy Names of Jesus and Mary have kept a chronicle of their work in Seattle for more than one hundred years. This chronicle gives us a first-hand account of the death of Bishop Junger, the collapse of the Cathedral's dome, and many other important events.

Museums also have many primary sources that tell the history of our state and our local communities, especially history museums like the Museum of Washington State History in Tacoma and the Museum of History and Industry in Seattle.

Secondary Sources. In addition to primary materials, the authors of this book used many secondary materials, like newspapers, websites, and books about the Catholic Church, Washington State, and Pacific Northwest history. One of the most important sources of information on day-to-day Catholic life is the Catholic Northwest Progress, which from 1908 until 2013, reported the news from a Catholic perspective.

Bishop Gerald Shaughnessy led the diocese through the Great Depression. (Courtesy of the Archives of the Catholic Archdiocese of Seattle)

Living Sources. We think of history being written on paper, like this book. But history is also found in other places. Our buildings— churches, schools, and hospitals— also say a lot about who we are. They show our priorities as a local Church and reflect our commitment to service. Inside and out, the art and architecture of our churches reveal what we believe and how we worship. Perhaps most importantly, the people who surround us in our parishes are a treasured living history of the Church in the Pacific Northwest. Talking to priests, religious, and lay Catholics, we add a whole new level to our understanding of what it has meant to be Catholic in the Pacific Northwest.

Miter belonging to Archbishop Connolly. (Courtesy of the Archives of the Catholic Archdiocese of Seattle)

Bishop A. M. A. Blanchet kept a diary of his journey from Montreal to Walla Walla in 1847. (Courtesy of the Archives of the Catholic Archdiocese of Seattle)

- **Find out more about the history of your parish church. When was it built? What is the community like? Has it changed over the years?**
- **Visit a history museum, either a small local history museum or one of the large ones like the Museum of History and Industry in Seattle. See what you discover. Can you find stories that overlap with the history told in this book?**
- **Interview someone who has been in your parish for a long time about their experiences.**
- **Ask your family members or friends about what their lives as Catholics have been like.**

TIMELINE

18th

1774 The first Catholic priests in the Pacific Northwest were Franciscans, part of the Perez expedition.

19th

1838 Father Francis Norbert Blanchet and Father Modeste Demers arrive at Fort Vancouver.

1839 F. N. Blanchet uses the Catholic Ladder during Holy Week at the Cowlitz Mission.

1846 Augustin Magloire Alexandre Blanchet (1797-1887) is ordained a bishop in St. James Cathedral, Montreal, for the new diocese of Walla Walla.

1847 On September 5, A. M. A. Blanchet arrives in Walla Walla.
The Whitman Massacre takes place on November 29.

1850 On May 31, Pope Pius IX creates the diocese of Nesqually. The diocese of Walla Walla is dissolved.

1851 Bishop Blanchet undertakes a "begging tour" to Mexico.

1852 Bishop Modeste Demers offers the first Mass in Seattle.

1856 Mother Joseph and Sisters of Providence arrive in Vancouver on December 8.

1857 Father Eugene Casimir Chirouse, OMI establishes a mission on the Tulalip Indian Reservation.

1867 Father Prefontaine builds Seattle's first Catholic Church, Our Lady of Good Help, at what is now 3rd Avenue and Washington Street in the Pioneer Square district.

1879 Aegidius Junger (1833-1895) becomes the second Bishop of Nesqually.

1885 St. James Cathedral, Vancouver is dedicated.

1891 The Jesuit Fathers establish Seattle College (now Seattle University).

1895 The Benedictine Fathers open St. Martin's College near Olympia.

1896 Edward O'Dea (1856-1932) becomes the third Bishop of Nesqually.

1897 The Klondike Gold Rush begins.

20th

1902 The first Council of the Knights of Columbus in Washington is organized.

1903 Bishop O'Dea moves from Vancouver to Seattle, making Our Lady of Good Help his pro-cathedral.

1903 Mother Frances Xavier Cabrini arrives in Seattle, establishing a home for orphans on Seattle's Beacon Hill.

1907 St. James Cathedral, Seattle, is dedicated on December 22.

1913 The Diocese of Spokane is established.

1920 Maryknoll Sisters establish a Japanese mission in Seattle.

1929 The stock market crash on October 29 marks the beginning of the Great Depression.

1933 Gerald Shaughnessy, SM (1887-1950) becomes the fourth Bishop of Nesqually.

1934 The first Serra Club is established.

1942 Executive Order 9066 orders the internment of Japanese Americans in camps.

1948	Thomas Arthur Connolly (1899-1991) is appointed coadjutor bishop, succeeding to the see upon Bishop Shaughnessy's death in 1950.
1950	The Catholic Youth Organization (CYO) is established.
1951	The diocese is elevated to the Archdiocese of Seattle. The diocese of Yakima is established.
1960	KOMO-TV begins production of Challenge, a religious public service program, featuring Father William Treacy and Rabbi Raphael Levine.
1962	Seattle sponsors the 47th Liturgical Conference at the Seattle World's Fair, anticipating many of the liturgical reforms of Vatican II.
1962	The first session of the Second Vatican Council begins on October 11. The Council will continue until December, 1965.

1968	The first Spanish-language Mass is celebrated at Immaculate Conception Parish, Seattle.
1975	Raymond Hunthausen (b. 1921) becomes the sixth bishop, second Archbishop of Seattle.
1987	Thomas Murphy (1932-1997) is appointed coadjutor Archbishop, succeeding to the see in 1991.
1997	Alexander Brunett (b. 1934) becomes the eighth bishop, fourth Archbishop of Seattle.

2000	During the Great Jubilee Year 2000, the Archdiocese of Seattle celebrates its sesquicentennial – 150 years since the diocese was established.
2010	J. Peter Sartain (b. 1952) becomes the ninth bishop, fifth Archbishop of Seattle.